Christmas Carols For Guitar

Graded arrangements of 12 favourite Christmas songs for acoustic, fingerstyle and classical guitar

Arranged by James Akers

Copyright © 2020 GMI - Guitar & Music Institute

www.guitarandmusicinstitute.com

ISBN 978-1-9163024-4-0

First published in Scotland in 2020 by GMI - Guitar & Music Institute

Christmas Carols For Guitar

Graded arrangements of 12 favourite Christmas songs for

acoustic, fingerstyle and classical guitar

Arranged by James Akers

Contents

Introduction

This book aims to provide guitarists of all levels with practical, appealing arrangements of well-known Christmas songs in both standard notation and tab. Each song appears in three versions. The first is simply the tune itself, set in a convenient key so that the beginner guitarist, in the early stages of their progress can give a convincing, recognisable rendition of the melody. This version includes chord symbols to allow for the beginner to be accompanied by a more experienced player or teacher or practise playing the chords themselves. The second version is the same melody with an added bass-line and occasional chords to allow the suggestion of harmony and provide more of a challenge to the advancing guitarist. This version employs a tonal harmonic idiom, as might be heard in traditional choral arrangements of these songs. The third version is a fully realised chordal arrangement with more advanced harmonies, utilising the full range of the fingerboard and a variety of techniques and idioms. This allows a more musically complete performance and should be a rewarding challenge for the accomplished player.

It is intended that this book will see the beginner guitarist through several years of study, allowing them to chart their progress over successive festive seasons and perform the tunes everyone wants to hear at Christmas. It is also intended to be a useful resource for teachers, providing them with a collection of pieces to suit pupils of all levels and technical requirements.

James Akers

Auld Lang Syne

Watch James perform the advanced version by pointing your mobile phone or tablet with a QR code reader at the box on the right.

Or go to the following URL:

https://www.youtube.com/watch?v=OzVBYqzKObM

Auld Lang Syne: Beginners

This tune is not a Christmas song but is commonly sung on new years' eve to celebrate the coming new year. It uses a pentatonic scale, which is often found in folk melodies from throughout the world and perhaps helps explains its international popularity.

Auld Lang Syne: Intermediate

This arrangement of Auld Lang Syne adds a bass-line and occasional three-part chords to accompany the melody. The implied harmony of the two-part texture stays largely within the key of G major, with only occasional chromatic passing notes to add variety.

Auld Lang Syne: Advanced

The advanced version of this piece has been set in a chord melody style, utilising more varied 'jazzy' chords and modulations and, in some places, a walking bass line to add to the rousing march-like feel of the arrangement. The challenge is to maintain the flow and projection of the melody while the other elements are being played.

Away in a Manger

Watch James perform the
advanced version by pointing
your mobile phone or tablet
with a QR code reader at the
box on the right.

Or go to the following URL:

https://www.youtube.com/watc
h?v=IH2Xgq7z5KQ

Away in a Manger: Beginners

This well-loved Christmas carol was written by the American composer William J. Kirkpatrick and first published in 1887 as *Luther's Cradle Hymn,* a reference to church reformer and amateur musician Martin Luther.

Away in a Manger: Intermediate

The intermediate version of Away in a Manger adds an active bass-line with frequent passing notes and modulations to give forward momentum to the rhythmically simple and static melody.

Away in a Manger: Advanced

This traditional carol has been arranged using a chromatic bassline and harmonies to reflect the gentleness of the text and the idea of an infant falling asleep while the world looks on.

Ding Dong Merrily on High

Watch James perform the advanced version by pointing your mobile phone or tablet with a QR code reader at the box on the right.

Or go to the following URL:

https://www.youtube.com/watch?v=ZHesv3Id3aI

Ding Dong Merrily on High: Beginners

The melody of *Ding Dong Merrily on High* was first published in the 16th century as a *Branle*, a lively Renaissance dance tune. It wasn't until 1924 it was adapted, with a text by George Ratcliffe, into a Christmas carol. It has proven enduringly popular in that form since.

Ding Dong Merrily On High: Intermediate

This lively arrangement employs a supportive bassline which clearly outlines the underlying harmony. During the long sequence in the second section the bass notes imply shifting key changes adding interest to the familiar melody.

Ding Dong Merrily On High: Advanced

This carol has been arranged as a study in natural harmonics, to sound like the bells of the text. By using a dropped D tuning, it is possible to play the complete melody, and bass line, using only natural harmonics. A short bell-like introduction has been added to establish the mood before the tune starts. This piece is quite demanding to play and should be a challenge to even the most advanced guitarists.

16

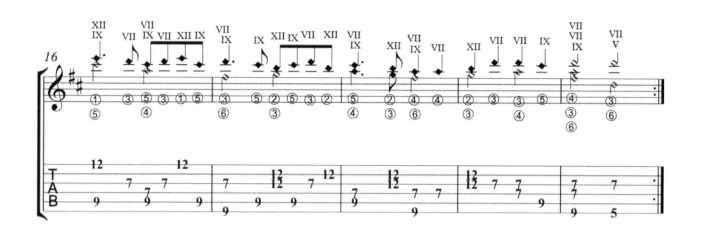

God Rest Ye Merry Gentlemen

Watch James perform the advanced version by pointing your mobile phone or tablet with a QR code reader at the box on the right.

Or go to the following URL:

https://www.youtube.com/watch?v=q6vl2C4fX0I

God Rest Ye Merry Gentlemen: Beginners

God Rest Ye Merry Gentlemen is another very old tune. The first published version dates from 1760 but the modal melody is most likely much older. It famously receives a mention in Charles Dickens' Christmas defining story A Christmas Carol, in which, upon hearing the first lines of the song, the novel's miserly protagonist, Ebeneezer Scrooge, picks up a ruler and attacks the singer with such energy that he is compelled to flee in terror.

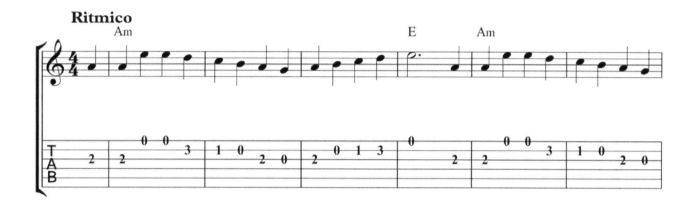

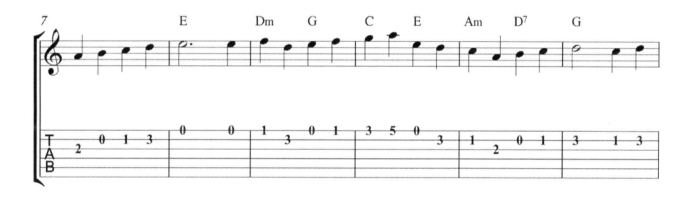

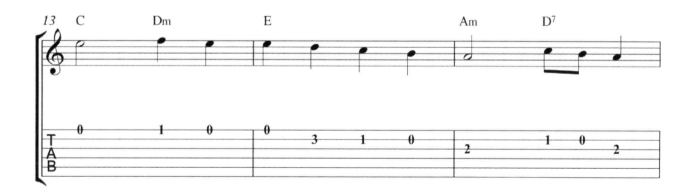

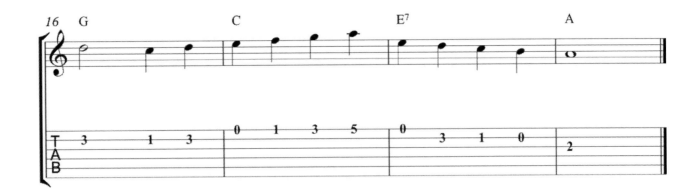

20

God Rest Ye Merry Gentlemen: Intermediate

This version of God Rest Ye Merry Gentlemen employs a bassline that is a mixture of implied harmony and consonant intervals, fitting with the modal sound of the tune.

Resolute

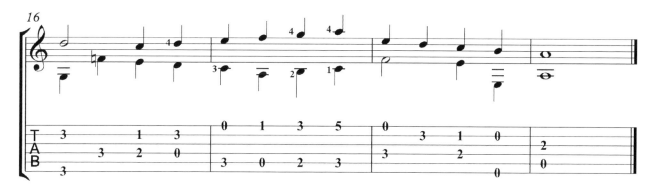

God Rest Ye Merry Gentlemen: Advanced

The harmonisation of his tune uses a descending chromatic bass, inspired by the Thelonius Monk classic Round Midnight, to reinforce the rise and fall of the melody and a pedal note in the last few bars to underpin the movement of the chords. The technical demands of this arrangement are in keeping the melody prominent while playing the more densely textured chords.

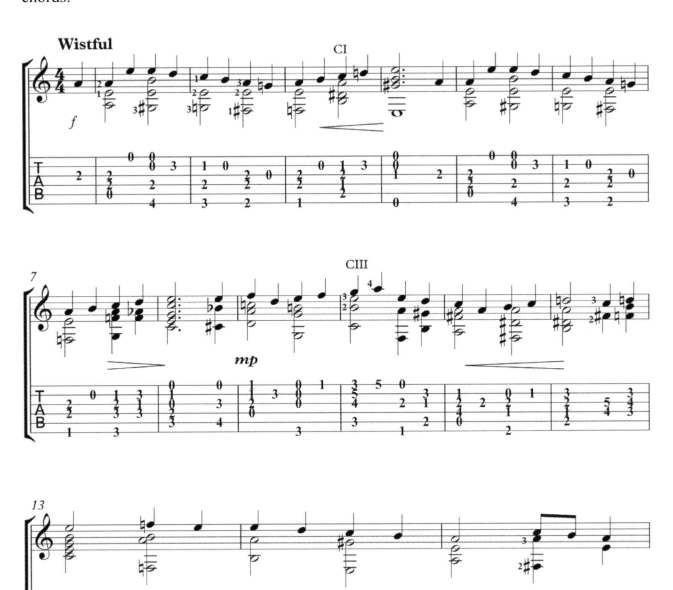

Good King Wenceslas

Watch James perform the advanced version by pointing your mobile phone or tablet with a QR code reader at the box on the right.

Or go to the following URL:

https://www.youtube.com/watch?v=7jPjZnwrAKc

Good King Wenceslas: Beginners

In a collection of old tunes, that of Good King Wenceslas is perhaps the oldest of all. It originally dates from the 13th century in the form of a spring carol, Tempus adest floridium. It was reworked in 1853 into its modern form telling the story of the saintly Duke of Bohemia, Wenceslaus.

Good Kind Wenceslas: Intermediate

The syllabic nature of Good King Wenceslas requires an active bass line to provide a satisfying harmonic underpinning to the melody. This should give the advancing guitarist an opportunity to exercise all their fingers.

Good King Wenceslas: Advanced

This arrangement of Good King Wenceslas is in the form of a passacaglia, in which the melody is underpinned by a repeated walking bass line, above which, the harmony changes to fit the tune. In nearly every bar the bass line remains the same, except in two instances, to provide variety. The challenge is to keep the bass line ringing out while giving a clear sense of the familiar melody.

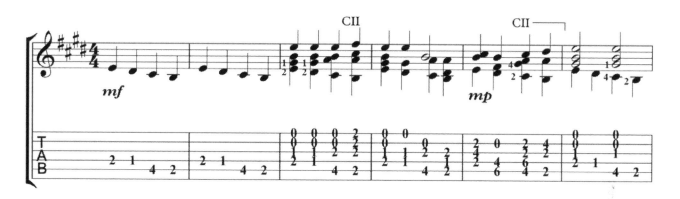

In Dulci Jubilo

Watch James perform the advanced version by pointing your mobile phone or tablet with a QR code reader at the box on the right.

Or go to the following URL:

https://www.youtube.com/watch?v=MU2nbgxgKNI

In Dulci Jubilo: Beginners

The tune of In Dulci Jubilo also dates from the 13th century and has appeared in many versions since that time. The composer Michael Praetorius used the tune repeatedly, it featured in a chorale prelude by the great J.S. Bach and was a hit for Mike Oldfield in 1975.

In Dulci Jubilo: Intermediate

In the two-part version of In Dulci Jubilo, the bassline, as well as harmonising the tune, provides a countermelody that is as active and rhythmic as the original melody.

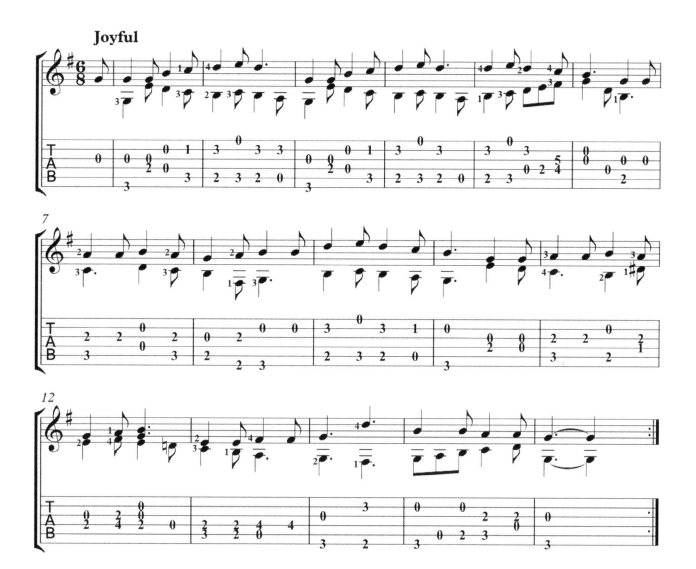

In Duci Jubilo: Advanced

This arrangement is influenced by techniques employed in Medieval and Renaissance music including drones, parallel fifths and false relations. The first part of the arrangement has the tune in the bass with repeated chords above as accompaniment. In the second half, the melody is in the treble with a varied chordal and arpeggiated accompaniment. When performed, some strumming or *rasgueados* could be added to the chords to add variety and excitement.

GET YOUR DOWNLOAD PACK WHICH SUPPORTS THIS PUBLICATION

1. Use a QR code reader and point at box below to download file.

2. OR paste this URL in a browser and then follow the download instructions:

https://gmiguitarshop.com/products/free-download-for-christmas-carols-for-guitar

3. OR go to https://gmiguitarshop.com and uses the search area at the top right of the website and search "Christmas Carols" and you'll see the download.

WHAT IS INCLUDED?

- Diagrams in PDF format of all chords played in each of the twelve beginner arrangements.

- mp3 files of all advanced version performances.

- Accompanying guitar tracks for all beginner arrangements.

PLEASE NOTE: The download is compressed by a utility programme named WINRAR which is commonly used by PC owners. If your PC does not see the compressed file, search "WINRAR DOWNLOAD" in your favourite browser to be directed to the main WINRAR website.

If you have a Mac computer, tablet or cell phone and encounter any difficulty opening the compressed file please use a search engine and search "opening WINRAR files on a Mac". There are many sites and Youtube videos which offer simple to execute ways on how to do this.

Jingle Bells

Watch James perform the advanced version by pointing your mobile phone or tablet with a QR code reader at the box on the right.

Or go to the following URL:

https://www.youtube.com/watch?v=R01tnkICftA

Jingle Bells: Beginners

This popular Christmas song dates from the 19th century and has been arranged here in a simpler form than the other pieces. The first version is suited to a young beginner, with enough of the tune to be recognisable but in a simplified form.

J.L.Pierpont

Jingle Bells: Intermediate

The intermediate version of Jingle Bells has the complete tune, also with chord symbols to allow for a second accompanying instrument.

J.L. Pierpoint

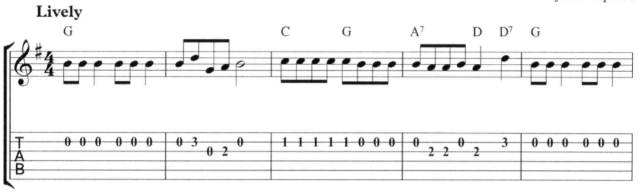

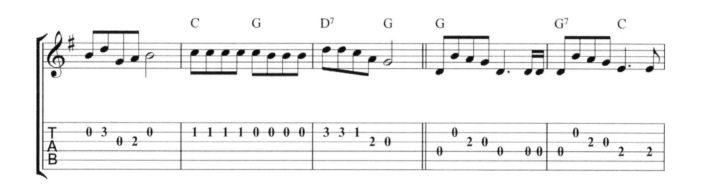

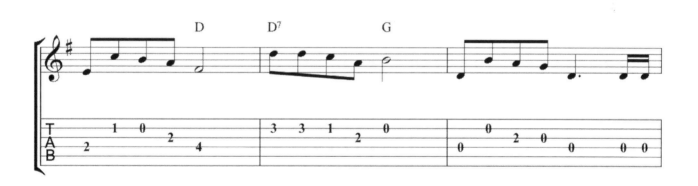

D.C. al Fine

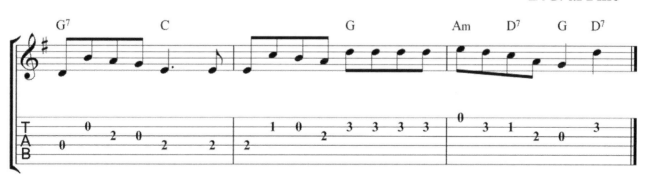

Jingle Bells: Advanced

The advanced arrangement of Jingle Bells is a relatively simple chord melody version without any complex modulations or excessive technical challenges, again, suited to a younger advancing player.

J.L. Pierpoint

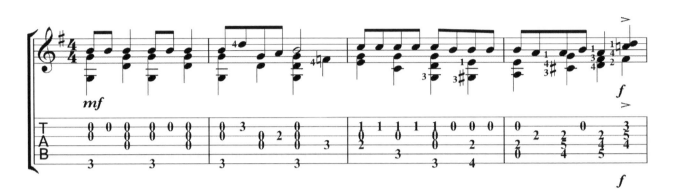

Fine

D.C. al Fine

O Christmas Tree

Watch James perform the advanced version by pointing your mobile phone or tablet with a QR code reader at the box on the right.

Or go to the following URL:

https://www.youtube.com/watch?v=IA3FhYNOz7U

O Christmas Tree: Beginners

O Christmas Tree, is a German Christmas song, *O Tannenbaum,* often sung in English translation. The melody is taken from a 16th century folk song which was unrelated to Christmas but was given a new text and lease of life in the 19th century.

O Christmas Tree: Intermediate

In the intermediate version of O Christmas Tree, the melody has been transposed to a higher key to allow for a more varied and satisfying melodic bass accompaniment.

O Christmas Tree: Advanced

The advanced version of this song uses a dropped d tuning to allow a pedal note, or drone, ostinato to underpin the melody. This produces some pleasing dissonances when combined with the gently chromatic chords harmonising the tune. In addition, there is an introduction and coda employing natural harmonic chords to add to the gentle wistful atmosphere of the piece.

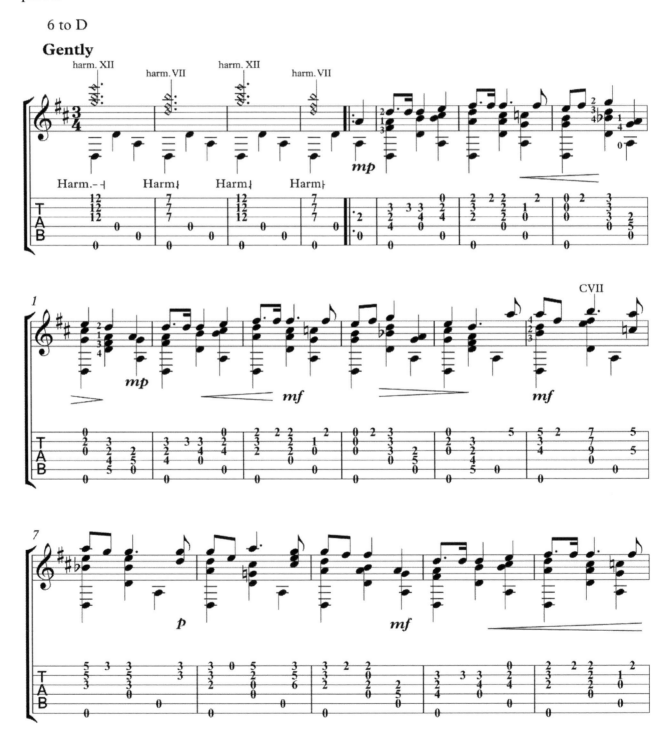

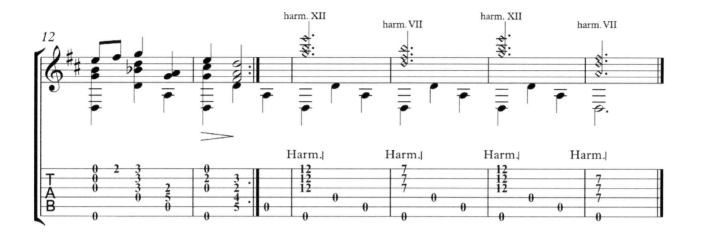

Silent Night

Watch James perform the advanced version by pointing your mobile phone or tablet with a QR code reader at the box on the right.

Or go to the following URL:

https://www.youtube.com/watch?v=mZZQ-ueI1lk

Silent Night: Beginners

Silent Night is perhaps the only well-known Christmas carol to have been composed specifically for guitar accompaniment. When the organ of the village church in Arnsdorf, Austria, was damaged by a flood in 1824, local schoolmaster Franz Xaver Guber quickly composed this tune to be sung with guitar accompaniment in the Christmas Eve service. It has remained a favourite Christmas song ever since.

Silent Night: Intermediate

Silent Night, in its intermediate form, uses a standard harmonisation which is implied by the choice of bass notes. these are intended to provide a warm and sonorous sound effect belying the simplicity of the texture.

Silent Night: Advanced

Gruber's original melody employed a simple diatonic harmonisation using arpeggiated guitar chords. This arrangement maintains the regular rhythm and undulating feel of the arpeggios but employs more complex harmonies, influenced by the great Paraguayan guitarist composer Agustín Barrios Mangoré.

Gruber

The Twelve days of Christmas

Watch James perform the advanced version by pointing your mobile phone or tablet with a QR code reader at the box on the right.

Or go to the following URL:

https://www.youtube.com/watch?v=tz0wtwmEjgA

The Twelve days of Christmas: Beginners

The melody of *The Twelve days of Christmas* was first adapted to the words in 1909. Both predate this publication by many years. It's a more complex tune than its popularity and familiarity might suggest with irregular phrase lengths and changes in time signature.

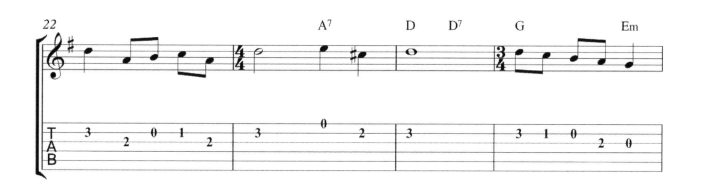

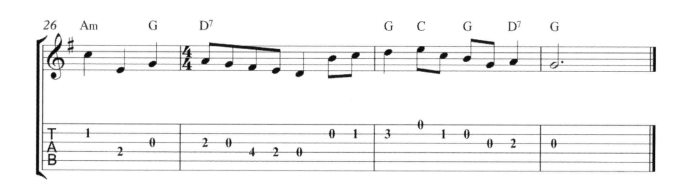

The Twelve Days of Christmas: Intermediate

One of the more demanding intermediate arrangements, The Twelve Days of Christmas, includes position shifts, bigger stretches and passages in tenths. These should help the evolving guitarist to develop their strength and coordination.

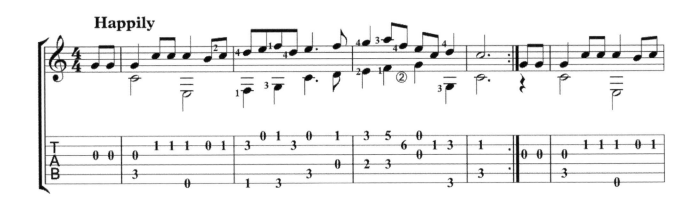

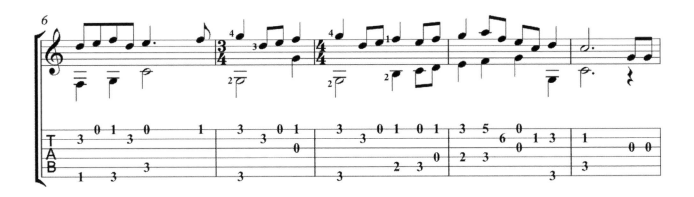

The Twelve Days of Christmas: Advanced

This arrangement is largely a study in consonant intervals, with the melody doubled either a sixth or third below and a walking bass line added. To play this version at the customary tempo should provide a challenge to most guitarists, with the many position shifts and atypical chord voicings.

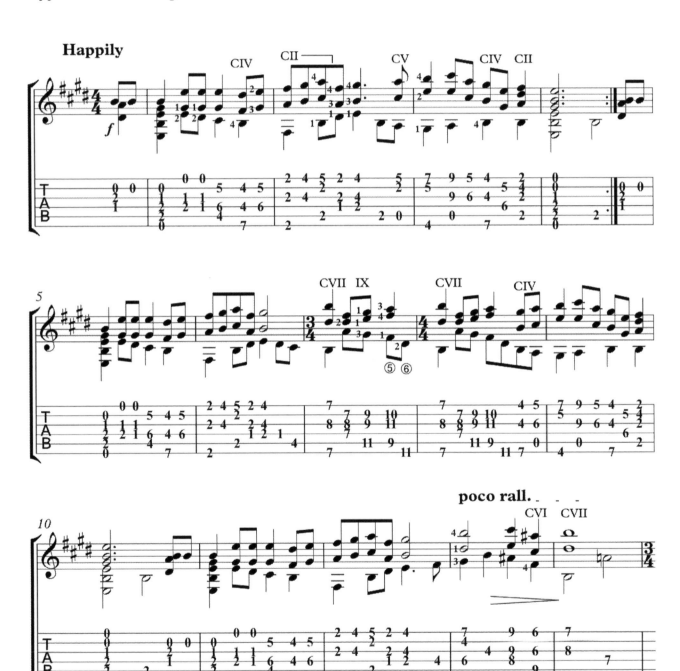

A Tempo

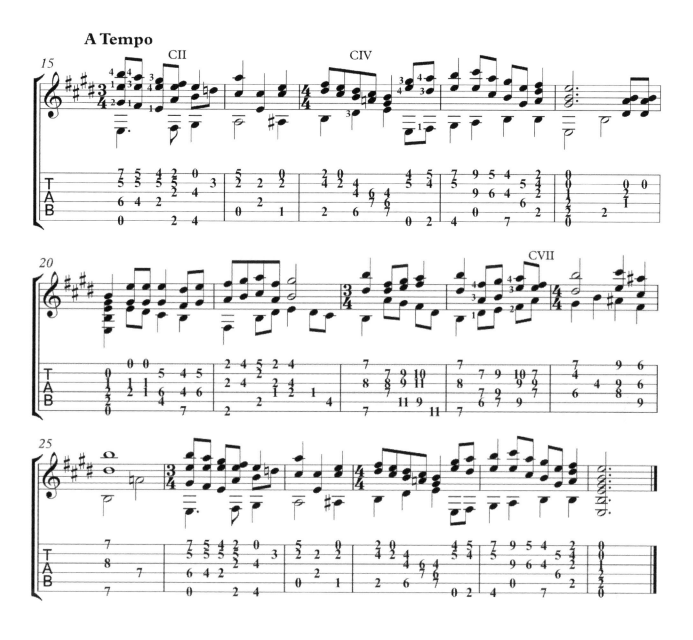

We Three Kings of Orient Are

Watch James perform the advanced version by pointing your mobile phone or tablet with a QR code reader at the box on the right.

Or go to the following URL:

https://www.youtube.com/watch?v=TVzPtxPd9Ew

We Three Kings of Orient Are: Beginners

We Three Kings of Orient Are, was composed for a Christmas pageant held at a seminary in New York in 1857. It proved so popular that it was published in 1863 and became the first non-European Christmas carol to achieve worldwide acclaim.

J.H.Hopkins

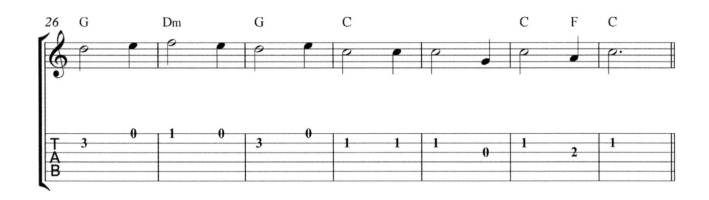

We Three Kings of Orient Are: Intermediate

We Three Kings is an unusual song in that it has long passages without melodic or harmonic change. An attempt has been made here to make these parts as resonant and consonant as possible to allow the intermediate guitarist and their audience to savour their beauty of tone.

J.H.Hopkins

We Three Kings of Orient Are: Advanced

The advanced version of this tune uses an arpeggiated accompaniment, such as might be found in the left hand of a piano piece. This enables the somewhat static harmonies in the second half of the tune to maintain some forward momentum and provides a technical challenge for the guitarist to sustain the melody while playing many other notes.

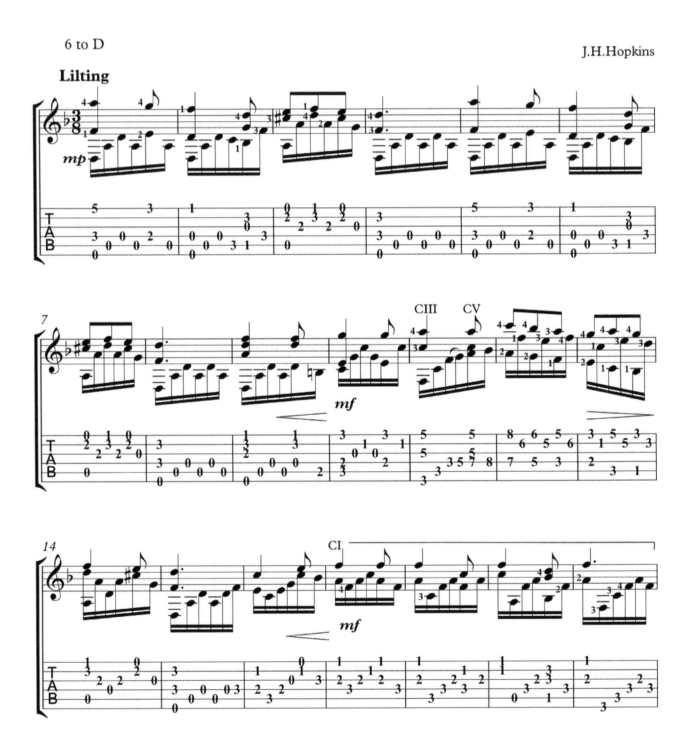

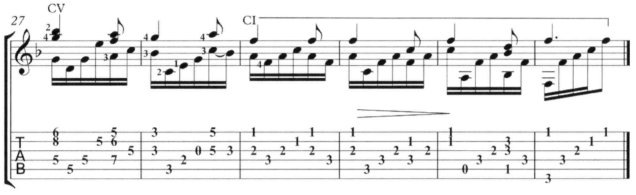

We Wish You a Merry Christmas

Watch James perform the advanced version by pointing your mobile phone or tablet with a QR code reader at the box on the right.

Or go to the following URL:

https://www.youtube.com/watch?v=TO5EQWcZG5k

We Wish You a Merry Christmas: Beginners

The origins of *We Wish You a Merry Christmas* are obscure. Similar texts are extant from the 19th century and the subject matter of the lyrics suggest an early date. However, the version of the tune so well-known today was first published in 1935 in an arrangement by Arthur Warrell.

We Wish You a Merry Christmas: Intermediate

The tune of We Wish You a Merry Christmas, has a rising chromatic bassline that brings life to the intermediate arrangement. Elsewhere, a walking bass is used to move the music forward while the tune is static.

We Wish You A Merry Christmas: Advanced

The tune of *We Wish You a Merry Christmas* is in three time and has been arranged here with a waltz-like accompaniment. The standard version of the tune already employs some chromatic harmonies which have been adapted and extended to add interest and complexity to this arrangement.

About James Akers

Critically acclaimed musician Jamie Akers was hailed as 'the great Scottish guitarist' by Classical Guitar Magazine and, in a review from Gramophone, his playing was described as, 'containing all the warmth, colour and expressive richness one could hope for.' Jamie has, throughout a varied career, explored various genres of music from a historical and stylistic perspective, combining diligent research with expressive performances to communicate the continuity of musical endeavour through the centuries.

Jamie was born in Scotland and began playing guitar at the age of 10. Initially playing rock and blues then attempting to play jazz and finally settling on the classical guitar, he was largely self-taught before having lessons with Robert Mackillop at Napier University, Edinburgh. Whilst at Napier he turned his attentions to playing the lute and pursued this as his principle study at the Royal College of Music, with Jakob Lindberg. Having added the Theorbo to his expanding instrument collection, Jamie completed his studies at Trinity College of Music, studying with Jacob Heringman and David Miller, with additional lessons and advice from Paul O'Dette and Elizabeth Kenny. Settled on the period instrument path, Jamie continued accumulating instruments and exploring the music of the 16th to 19th centuries, with occasional forays into contemporary music.

Following a Junior Fellowship at Trinity College of Music Jamie began pursuing a varied professional career. As a soloist he has performed throughout Europe, the Middle East and Australia, giving recitals at the Edinburgh Fringe Festival, Ullapool Guitar Festival, Classical Guitar Retreat, Exeter Guitar Festival, the Yorke Music Trust, the Italian Cultural Institute, in the L'Oratoire de Lourve, and the Copenhagen Renaissance Music Festival.

He has accompanied leading singers including Dame Emma Kirkby, James Laing, Miriam Allan, Claire Wilkinson and Jake Arditti and is the staff accompanist for the John Kerr memorial song prize. Jamie has performed with many early music ensembles such as I Fagiolini, Ex Cathedra, Stile Antico, the Marian Consort, Fretwork, Chelys Viol Consort, The Rose Consort of Viols, The Parley of Instruments, The Hanover Band, The Brook Street Band, Sounds Baroque and the Dunedin Consort.

As a continuo player Jamie has worked for major opera companies, English National Opera, Welsh National Opera, Opera North, Longborough festival opera and Innsbruck Festival Opera and orchestras and chamber groups including The Scottish, Irish and English Chamber Orchestras, Northern Sinfonia, the Royal Scottish National Orchestra, The Ulster Orchestra, The Essen Philharmonie, The Scottish Ensemble, with trumpeter Alison Balsom, and ventured into indie folk-rock with Damon Albarn.

Jamie has performed on numerous recordings; a few film soundtracks; several theatrical stages, including Shakespeare's Globe Theatre and the Barbican, and broadcast for the BBC, France Musique and RTE Lyric, Ireland, and has been an artist in residence with the renowned Scottish Ensemble.

Jamie lectures in early plucked strings at the Royal Conservatoire of Scotland and teaches annually on the Renaissance Music Week course in Ejstrupholm, Denmark. He has also taught or given masterclasses at, The Royal College of Music, The Royal Northern College of Music, The Royal Welsh College of Music and Drama, the Western Australian Academy of Performing Arts and The Rostov Conservatoire, Russia.

http://jamieakers.com/

More From James Akers From GMI - Guitar & Music Institute

If you have enjoyed this book then we're sure you will also find James's transcriptions of Theorbo music for classical guitar a must buy.

Not only does the book include beautiful works by Kapsberger, Piccinini and Castaldi but this large publication also includes the following:

All works offered in both music and guitar tabulature.

Selected works include an audio commentary that is accessed via QR codes placed alongside specific titles. Use your mobile (cell) phone or tablet to listen to James's commentary from both a technical and musical perspective about the work you will be learning.

Selected works include a QR code that opens up a performance video of the piece currently being considered. Listen to this stellar guitarist play and interpret the musical composition for your guidance as well as listening pleasure.

Owners of the book will be able to access further musical works that accompany this publication. Your copy of this book will include a code which enables you to access this PDF download completely free of charge.

Italian Theorbo Music is available to purchase from Amazon and all other good online sellers in both printed and electronic format. A wire bound flat lie version of the book is available only from https://gmiguitarshop.com

An introduction PDF book containing extra works for pre sale of this book or as mentioned free for those who have already purchased the printed version is available to buy direct from the GMI - Guitar & Music Institute online shop at https://gmiguitarshop.com

RECORDING

James Akers' critically acclaimed recording of Scottish Romantic Guitar Music, The Soldier's Return, is available on CD and through various digital platforms.

Visit www.resonusclassics.com for more information.

ENJOYED THIS BOOK? CHECK OUT THE SECOND BOOK IN THE SERIES!

James Akers first Christmas Carols book for guitar was such a success that, in conjunction with GMI worked throughout 2021 to create a second book of family favourite Carols for guitar.

We've kept exactly the same format which is detailed overleaf, but this book is bigger coming in at ninety four pages and the arrangements at advanced level will really text guitar players around the world.

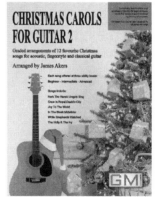

CHRISTMAS CAROLS FOR GUITAR 2

The second book in the series of graded arrangements of 12 all time favorite Christmas songs for acoustic, fingerstyle and classical guitar players.

A further collection of twelve of the most well known and loved Christmas carols and holiday season songs beautifully arranged for guitar by guitarist James Akers.

Each of the 12 songs are offered at beginner, intermediate and advanced technical versions. For beginners, start with the easy version of the song, then build up to the more complex versions which are all found in this book. This publication would also be an excellent resource for guitar teachers looking for potential material for students around Christmas time.

This book offers

All songs are notated in both music and guitar TAB for non music readers.

All advanced versions of the song come with QR codes for watching a video performance of each song.

THE TWELVE SONGS INCLUDED ARE:

Deck the Halls

Hark the Herald Angels Sing

I Saw Three Ships

In the Bleak Midwinter

Joy To The World

O Come All Ye Faithful

O Little Town Of Bethlehem

Once In Royal David's City

The Coventry Carol

The First Nowell

The Holly and The Ivy

While Shepherds Watched Their Flocks

Plus a bonus mystery song!

FREE DOWNLOAD OF EXTRA MATERIAL

A link is included within the book to download free extra material which accompanies the publication. Contents of the free download are:

mp3 versions of all advanced versions of the Christmas carol guitar arrangements for you to listen to before practice.

mp3 accompanying tracks for the beginner versions of the Christmas carols for play along.

A PDF book which details all the chords used in the beginner guitar chord arrangements offered in chord diagram format for easy understanding.

Another Great Title By James Akers From GMI - Guitar & Music Institute

If you have enjoyed this book then we're sure you will also find James's transcriptions found in Scottish Classical Guitar Collection Volume 1 an absolute must have.

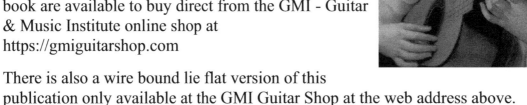

For the intermediate to advanced player, this volume of work includes Mauro Giuliani's beautiful settings of six favourite Scottish songs; Fernando Sor's masterful 'Variations on Ye Banks and Braes' and Johan Kaspar Mertz's dramatic evocation of the landscape of the Outer Hebrides, 'Fingal's Cave.'

Scottish Classical Guitar Collection Volume 1 is available to purchase from Amazon and all other good online sellers in both printed and electronic format. PDF versions of individual songs found within the book are available to buy direct from the GMI - Guitar & Music Institute online shop at https://gmiguitarshop.com

There is also a wire bound lie flat version of this publication only available at the GMI Guitar Shop at the web address above.

If you enjoyed this publication, then please visit the following websites for more content, lessons, articles, videos, podcasts, free and paid content and more…

We'd also really appreciate a positive review on Amazon if you found this book enjoyable and an addition to your guitar playing experience.

www.guitarandmusicinstitute.com

gmiguitarshop.com

USING THE QR CODES...WHAT'S A QR CODE READER?

If you are not familiar with a QR code, it's the box shown on every title page of a song and has strange marks on it.

Using a search engine of your choice, type in "free QR code reader", there are many to choose from. Select one and download it to your cell/mobile phone or tablet.

Once installed, open the app up and point it at one of the squares, keeping your hand steady. It will recognise the web address in the box and notify you once it has worked it's magic.

It will offer to open up the video that has been added to the QR box you are pointing at. You can watch and listen to the song or use the opened video to play along with the song.

Printed in Great Britain
by Amazon